The Usborne
Write Your
Own Story
Word Book

heroic adventures

wild and free

unexpected dangers

billowing waves

daring

intrepid

brave and bold

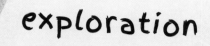

exploration

deep sea

mysterious

sea monster

cavernous

unknown territory

obscured vision

long

way

down

stay
very
calm

murky depths

The Usborne
Write Your Own Story Word Book

With *Inspiring Ideas* by
Jane Bingham

Sensational Illustrations by
Kyle Beckett and Amy Marie Stadelmann

Inventive Designs by
Stephanie Jeffries

and *Fabulous Words* chosen by

....

Write your name here.

Contents

Discover the amazing power of words.

Choosing words

Pick the best words for your stories.

Creating characters

Paint portraits with words.

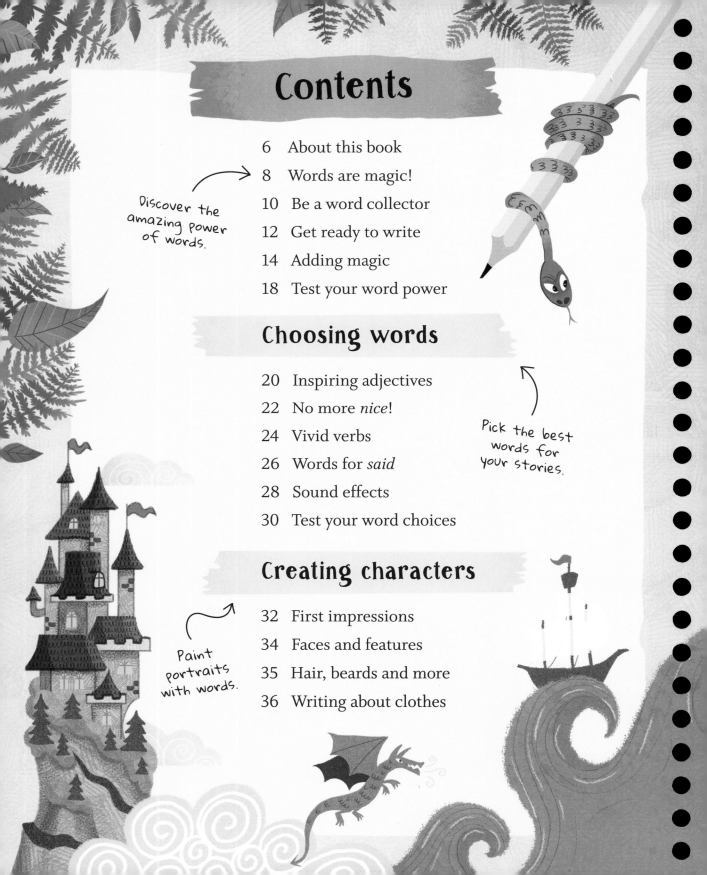

ZAP!

Setting the scene

Create convincing settings.

Words for stories

Use word prompts to write fantastic stories.

POP!

resplendent
glowing
precious
glistening

About this book

Do you sometimes struggle to find the words you need to make your story come to life? Then this is the book for **YOU**.

Look inside for hundreds of...

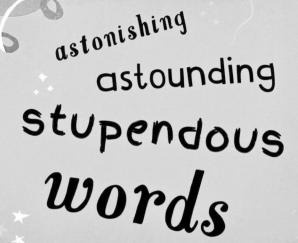

astonishing
astounding
stupendous
words

Use this book to help you...

Collect and choose words

accumulate

assemble

Pages 8–30

Create convincing characters

curious

lanky

obstinate

Pages 32–46

Set the scene for your story

clammy

echoing

musty

Pages 48–58

Use enticing story words

galaxy

ogre

poltergeist

Pages 60–92

And there's **plenty of space for your writing,** too.

As you work your way through the book, you'll **improve** your word skills and **expand** your vocabulary.

What words should I use to describe you?

You could try...

flexible

energetic

supple

acrobatic

Look out for writing tips wherever you see this symbol.

Build your own collection of inspiring words and phrases.

wondrous

illusion

mystical

glimmer

Go online at Usborne Quicklinks

There's a wealth of useful resources on the internet to help you with your writing. At Usborne Quicklinks, you'll find links to websites where you can learn a new word every day or try out puzzles and challenges to increase your word power. You can also watch videos packed with unusual words and take virtual tours of exciting story settings.

For links to all these sites, go to:
usborne.com/Quicklinks
and type in 'story word book'.

Words are magic!

Choosing the right words for your stories is like sprinkling magic dust over them. Take a look at this page to see how some carefully chosen words can transform a scene.

Archie searched the attic until he saw a chest. Beside it was a key. He turned the key in the lock and the chest opened. It was full of coins and jewels!

This is so dull!

Archie <u>rummaged</u> through the <u>gloomy</u> attic until he <u>spotted</u> a <u>dusty</u> wooden chest. <u>Lying half-hidden</u> beside it was a <u>huge, golden</u> key. <u>Nervously,</u> he turned the key in the lock and the chest <u>creaked</u> open <u>very slowly.</u> It was <u>heaped</u> to the brim with <u>glittering</u> coins and jewels!

Much better!

Here's what happens next in the story...

At the bottom of the chest was a piece
of paper. It had writing on it.

Try rewriting these sentences, using EXCITING words.
The words below should help.

scroll   scrawled signature

spidery writing

faded ink   secret symbols

crumpled map   smudges

buried treasure   indecipherable

Be a word collector

All good story writers are word collectors – and you can be one too. Get into the habit of noting down words and phrases that you like. It could be the start of a writing habit that stays with you for life.

Books, comics and magazines are filled with wonderful words.

Once you start looking out for interesting words, you'll spot them everywhere.

invincible

galumphing

hullabaloo

electrifying

You'll find some intriguing words and phrases online.

Serendipity

aura

invertebrate

translucent

Use a dictionary

Whenever you come across an unfamiliar word, check its meaning in a dictionary. Then think about how you could use it in your writing.

Be aware of striking words in movies and on TV.

celebrity

quizzical

interlude

syncopate

kerfuffle

persnickety

Listen to conversations to learn some surprising words.

bamboozle

These words will be perfect for my collection!

How preposterous!

Frankly, I'm flabbergasted!

cold	collapse	collect	collection
chilly	crumble	accumulate	assortment
cool	disintegrate	amass	batch
crisp	give way	assemble	heap
freezing	sag	gather	hoard
	slump	hoard	mass
		stockpile	pile
		store	stack

Try a thesaurus

A thesaurus can help you find new words for your stories. Look up a word you already know, and you'll see a list of **synonyms** – words and phrases with a similar meaning.

Get ready to write

A good way to get started on a story is to think about the words you'd like to use. Collecting words will help kick-start your imagination – and your words will inspire you as you write.

Think about **story types**, **characters** and **settings**.

Story types

- space
- spies
- school
- ghosts
- fantasy

A DANGEROUS MISSION

top secret
undercover
coded message
hidden clues
enemy agent
narrow escape

Add your own words here.

SAM SMITH, SUPER SPY

fearless
charming
poker-faced
ruthless
catlike
super cool

Characters

- pirate
- princess
- trapeze artist
- inventor
- secret agent

You could look at pictures for extra inspiration...

...and maybe draw a map of your story's setting.

unexplored territory

impassable jungle

bottomless lagoon

menacing mountains

stinking swamp

rugged reef

Settings

- castle
- (tropical island)
- desert
- jungle
- city
- distant planet
-
-
-

There's room for more settings here.

AN ISLAND HIDEAWAY

deserted beach

underground lair

luxury villa

flooded cave

rocket launch pad

submarine dock

You'll find sections on **characters, settings** and **story types** later in this book.

Adding magic

Once you've written a first draft of your story, it's time to get to work on editing your writing. This is your chance to add some _word magic!_

Take a careful look at all the words you've used. Then ask yourself these questions:

Am I using _inspiring_ adjectives?

Read about **adjectives** on pages 20–23.

Have I chosen _vivid_ verbs?

Learn about **verbs** on pages 24–27.

Can I use **stronger** sounding words?

Find out about **sound effects** on pages 28–29.

Should I swap a word for an _exciting_ phrase?

Can I change the order of my words to make them flow more **smoothly**?

Should I slow down the pace of my words to add _suspense_?

Writing stories is a three-stage process:

1 Plan your story. ✓

2 Write your draft. ✓

3 Edit your draft until your story is perfect.

Make it sparkle!

Editing your story is like polishing a gem to make it sparkle. Most writers spend more time on editing than on any other stage of their writing!

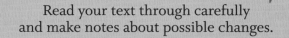

Read your text through carefully
and make notes about possible changes.

First draft

The time machine (landed.) ← Too dull! Add an interesting phrase.

The doors <u>opened</u> and Jem <u>looked</u> outside. ← Use some vivid verbs.

The first thing she saw was a (big) footprint. ← Find a better adjective.

She felt the ground (move.) ← Choose a more dramatic word.

Then she heard a (big) roar. ← Think of a powerful alternative.

She <u>felt scared.</u> ← Go for a gripping phrase.

Hmmmm. That's not very exciting.

Second draft

The time machine landed <u>with a resounding thud.</u>

The doors <u>slid open</u> and Jem <u>peered</u> outside.

The first thing she saw was a <u>gigantic</u> footprint.

She felt the ground <u>shudder.</u>

Then she heard a <u>bloodcurdling</u> roar.

<u>Icy shivers ran down her spine.</u>

What a transformation!

This story is much more dynamic than it was, but maybe you'd still like to make some changes?

Second draft

Create a surprising opening.

The time machine landed with a resounding thud.

Slow down the action to build suspense.

The doors slid open and Jem peered outside.

The first thing she saw was a gigantic footprint.

She felt the ground shudder.

Then she heard a bloodcurdling roar.

Icy shivers ran down her spine.

There's room on this page for you to add your own notes.

Write out your version of the story so far.
Then describe what happens next.

Third draft

CRASH! The time machine landed with a resounding thud. Very slowly, the doors slid open...

I just can't wait to read the rest of the story!

17

TEST YOUR WORD POWER

Time yourself!

Ready... Set... GO!

Pick a common word like *hot* or *cold* and set a timer. How many synonyms for your word can you list in two minutes?

Check your answers in a thesaurus. If you're playing with friends, the winner is the one with the most synonyms, and you can add extra points for interesting words.

A synonym is a word that means exactly or nearly the same as another word.

blistering
steamy
sweltering

chilly
freezing
perishing

Switch the mood

This activity uses the power of words to change the mood of a story. Imagine you've reached a secret forest. Is it threatening or welcoming?

First, describe the forest using words and phrases that create a sense of menace.

shadowy, wreathed in mist,

Then, describe the same forest, this time using words and phrases to evoke a sense of peace.

dappled shade, sunlit glade,

This challenge also works well for descriptions of people, animals and objects.

Fun with words

Crosswords, wordsearches and word-building games are all great ways to increase your word power. Challenge yourself or play a game with friends.

Choosing words

scintillating

thrilling

remarkable

captivating

Inspiring adjectives

If you keep using the same tired old adjectives,
your readers will soon lose interest, but a few arresting
words can make your writing come to life.

Oh no, not **big, bad** and **ugly** again...

WARNING!

BIG, BAD, UGLY DRAGON

NO WAY!
I'm **gigantic**,
horrendous and
hideous!
RAARRRR!

Here are some words you could use to describe...

... a **good** book
absorbing
captivating
outstanding
remarkable
thrilling

... a **big** building
enormous
huge
massive
sprawling
vast

... a **bad** movie
appalling
atrocious
dismal
dreadful
terrible

... a **small** insect
microscopic
miniscule
minute
teeny
tiny

... a **beautiful** movie star
attractive
gorgeous
radiant
striking
stunning

Use the extra
space on each
shield to add
some adjectives
of your own.

Now you've started to think about interesting words, try adding more adjectives to these descriptions.

Don't be afraid to choose unusual words!

Adventures could be described as...

action-packed
nerve-wracking
perilous

A puppy might be...

mischievous
playful
rambunctious

A fairground ride may be...

exhilarating
hair-raising
nail-biting

Some words for **the night sky** are...

inky
pitch-black
starry

A monster may be...

bloodthirsty
ferocious
hairy

Circle the adjectives you like most, and write your own list here.

Some sensational adjectives are...

A cave could feel...

clammy
claustrophobic
dank

It's actually quite cozy!

21

No more *nice!*

Nice is the most boring adjective of all, but it's a word we use all the time. Next time you find yourself writing *nice*, think about what you REALLY want to say. Then pick a scintillating word instead!

POSTCARD

Dear Louis,

I had a (nice) time last week with my (nice) friend. The weather was (nice), the view was (nice) and we had a (nice) picnic.

Love from Amma x

Louis Smart

The Old School House

2 Colle

Book

Why would you ever use *nice* when there are so many STUPENDOUS words to choose from?

Look at these alternatives and circle the ones you like most.

a nice time	a nice friend
amazing	considerate
awesome	delightful
enjoyable	fun-loving
excellent	generous
extraordinary	kind
fabulous	lively
fantastic	lovely
terrific	sympathetic
unforgettable	wonderful

nice weather	a nice view	a nice picnic
beautiful	breathtaking	appetizing
bright	impressive	delicious
fair	magnificent	mouth-watering
fine	picturesque	scrumptious
glorious	sensational	tasty
mild	spectacular	yummy
pleasant	splendid	
sunny	stunning	
warm	superb	

Now try rewriting the postcard
to Louis, using INSPIRING words.

POSTCARD

Dear Louis,

Louis Smart

The Old School House

2 Coll

Bo

Choose from the
words on these pages
and add some more
of your own.

23

Vivid verbs

Verbs tell you what people do, think or feel, and everyone does things in their own special way. You can express your character's personality by using some carefully chosen verbs.

Sit

perch
sit bolt upright
slouch
sprawl

Other ways to walk

meander
plod
saunter
stroll
strut
swagger
wander

Jump

bounce
bound
hurdle
leap
spring
vault

Walk slowly

amble
dawdle
hobble
shuffle
stagger
totter
trudge
waddle

Walk quickly

march
pace
stomp
stride

Which verbs do you like best? Draw a circle around them.

Run

dash
charge
hurtle
jog
race
scamper
sprint
trot

Climb

ascend
clamber
scale
scrabble
scramble
shimmy up

There's room for you to add extra verbs to these lists.

Can you choose verbs to fit these characters?

Laugh
cackle
chortle
chuckle
giggle
guffaw
snicker
titter

How would a monster eat and drink?

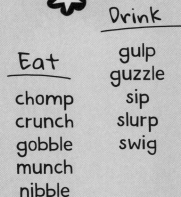

How would an evil genius laugh?

Eat
chomp
crunch
gobble
munch
nibble

Drink
gulp
guzzle
sip
slurp
swig

Adverb alert!

People often use adverbs, such as *loudly* or *quickly*, to adjust the meaning of a verb, but if you use too many adverbs, your writing can sound clunky. If possible, choose a precise verb instead of an adverb.

This sentence sounds rather awkward:

Arthur shouted loudly and ran quickly back home.

This one has much more impact:

Arthur <u>bellowed</u> and <u>raced</u> back home.

Words for *said*

Did you know that the English language has at least 300 verbs that can be used instead of *said*? Here are some alternatives to choose from.

Which words do you think work best? You could circle them.

Matt...
commented
mentioned
observed
pointed out
remarked

It's raining again.

I'm just so bored!

Zara...
complained
groaned
grumbled
moaned
sighed

Carrie...
asked
demanded
inquired
queried
questioned

What have you got there?

It's a surprise.

Omar...
answered
replied
responded
retorted

Poppy...
cried
sobbed
wailed
whimpered
whined

My party is ruined!

It was an accident.

Amy...
asserted
insisted
maintained
protested

Bertie...
announced
declared
proclaimed
stated

I'm leaving home!

Please don't go!

Auntie...
begged
beseeched
implored
pleaded

I'm the greatest!

Stop showing off!

Ziggy...
boasted
bragged
claimed
crowed
gloated

Josh...
bellowed
growled
roared
snapped
snarled

Can you follow each of these speeches with an alternative to **said**?

I just want to get out!

There's a giant bee!

I feel sick.

Don't overdo it!

Alternatives to *said* can be useful, but use them sparingly. DON'T replace *said* every time someone speaks.

Nathan... _____

Jamila... _____

Carl... _____

Sound effects

You can have fun using words to create dramatic sound effects. Read this description out loud and listen to the sounds made by words working together.

> Jo cowered inside her tent as the storm raged around her.
>
> The rain (b)ucketed down, and the tent was (b)attered and (b)uffeted by the wind.
>
> (Crack, boom, rumble) went the thunder.
>
> (Bright) flashes of (light)ning made the (sky) seem (light) as day.

The repeated **b** sounds at the start of the words make the rain and wind feel relentless.

Repeating sounds at the start of words is called **alliteration**.

These words sound like the noises they're describing.

Using words to imitate sounds is called **onomatopoeia**.

The repeated **i** sounds inside the words create a sense of brightness.

Repeating vowel sounds inside words is called **assonance**.

You'll find more storm words on page 83.

Now try using sound effects to describe a firework display.
(The words on this page should help.)

whistle
whizz
whoosh
flicker
flash
splutter
shower
burst
bang
pop

First write about
the fireworks.

scream
squeal
shiver
gasp
gulp
gape

Then describe the
reactions of the crowd.

Make your
writing sparkle
with **alliteration**,
assonance and
onomatopoeia!

TEST YOUR WORD CHOICES

Adjective alphabet

You can play this game with friends or challenge yourself.

1. Pick something to describe – it could be an object, a person, an animal or a place.

2. Work your way through the alphabet, each time choosing an adjective that starts with the next letter.

You'll need to skip the tricky letters x and z.

My pet kitten is...

adventurous   brave   cuddly   dozy   excitable

Verbs into stories

Cut up 16 or more scraps of paper and write a verb on each one. Pick four out of a hat, and write a short story using those verbs. Then try again with four new verbs.

You can make the game more challenging by choosing unusual words.

HOVER

IMAGINE

MUMBLE

ZOOM

Story-building

In this game, players take turns to draw random words out of a hat.

invention

juggle

Player 1 draws a word and uses it in the opening sentence of a story.

Player 2 draws the next word and uses it in the story's second sentence.

The more words you put in the hat, the longer your story will be.

grumpy

enchanting

powerful

fearful

Creating characters

First impressions

How do you introduce your characters to your readers? It's useful to picture them walking towards you and ask yourself what you notice first.

squat

lofty

These words will help you describe your characters as if you're seeing them for the very first time.

lanky
leggy
statuesque
towering

bony
skinny
slender
slim

dainty
elfin
petite
pint-sized
tiny

spindly
sylphlike
trim
willowy

Learning from the movies

Movie directors often show a distant shot of a character before the camera zooms in to reveal more detail.

"My kind of people"

TAKE	SCENE
3	18

Use this space to describe a character you've invented.

Gradually, a figure emerged from the mist...

Characters don't have to be human!
Can you give your first impressions of a dinosaur?

_____

_____

_____

_____

Choose from the words on these pages and add more of your own.

chubby	beefy	bent
plump	burly	hunched
portly	hefty	slouched
pudgy	hulking	slumped
roly-poly	muscular	
rotund	stocky	straight-backed
stout	strapping	upright
tubby	thickset	

diminutive

Now imagine a robot heading towards you.
What words would you use to describe it?

_____

_____

_____

_____

First impressions often include the way a character moves. You'll find lots of words for walk and run on page 24.

33

Faces and features

How do you paint a portrait with words?
The words on this page will help.

DESCRIBING FACES

baby-faced   oval
craggy   round
dumpy   smooth-skinned
freckled   square-jawed
heart-shaped   unshaven
long   wrinkled

There's room to add words to these lists.

EYES
bloodshot
bulging
deep-set
glaring
kind
piercing
sparkling
staring
twinkling

EYEBROWS
arched
bristly
bushy
delicate

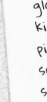

MOUTHS
curving
full-lipped
gaping
pouting
rosebud
smiling
sulky
wide

NOSES
beaky
button
crooked
hooked
pointed
snub
turned-up

TEETH
- broken   - pearly white
- even   - protruding
- gleaming   - yellow

Hair, beards and more

What kind of hair do your characters have? Is it wispy and mousy or frizzy and red? Or maybe one of your characters is completely bald?

auburn
black
blonde
chestnut
iron gray
silver
snowy white

- flowing beard
- goatee
- mustache
- sideburns
- stubble

braids
bun
cornrows
crew cut
dreadlocks
pigtails
ponytail
pudding bowl
quiff

Circle the words on these pages that fit your story's characters.

curly
disheveled
floppy
spiky
straight
tangled
wavy
windswept
wiry

 ## What do they look like?

Sometimes a comparison can add interest to your descriptions.

He looked like a friendly owl.

Her hair was a beautiful bird's nest.

35

Writing about clothes

The clothes that characters wear reveal a lot about them. These pages are packed with clothing words to use in your descriptions.

All kinds of clothes

- designer jeans
- embroidered coat
- floral nightgown
- leopard print bodysuit
- purple overalls
- sari
- sarong
- striped pajamas
- tailcoat
- tartan kilt
- three-piece suit
- trench coat

Clothes can be...

- baggy
- bulky
- figure-hugging
- flowing
- frilly
- fussy
- padded
- silky
- skintight
- stiff
- swirling
- tailored

Clothes can look...

- crisply ironed
- elegant
- fashionable
- flamboyant
- flattering
- glamorous
- neat
- old-fashioned
- scruffy
- sporty
- worn-out

HATS ETC.

beanie
boater
deerstalker
fascinator
flat cap
hijab
sou'wester
top hat
turban

MATERIALS

chunky corduroy
crushed velvet
faded denim
fake fur
itchy wool
shimmering satin
soft suede

SHOES ETC.

furry slippers
sandals
sneakers
stilettos
work boots

What kind of clothes do you imagine your characters wearing? Try describing them here.

You can make your characters really stand out by giving them some unusual items of clothing.

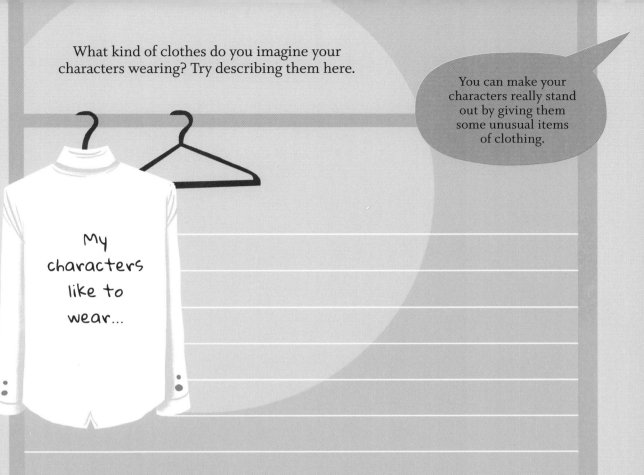

My characters like to wear...

Clothes from the past

If you use the right names for historical costumes, your stories will feel much more convincing – and you'll learn some wonderful words!

spats
cravat
button boots
petticoat
breeches
silk-lined cape
crinoline
parasol

army greatcoat
monocle
jerkin
hobnail boots
bloomers
lace shawl
knickerbockers
ballgown

Personality words

Which words would you choose to sum up the characters in your story?
Aim to use precise, interesting words like the ones shown here.

Circle the words
you'd most like to use
in your writing.

serene
easy-going
tranquil

nosy
inquisitive
curious

confident
extrovert
poised

snobbish
haughty
snooty

dreamy
imaginative
thoughtful

amusing
entertaining
witty

stubborn
headstrong
obstinate

caring
warm-hearted
affectionate

arrogant
boastful
conceited

cunning
deceitful
devious

spiteful
malicious
mean

bashful
retiring
shy

Personality in action

Descriptive words like these are
very useful, but they're not enough
on their own. The best way to show
personality is through the things your
characters do, say and think.

Think of a character for a story. Then choose some personality words to fit that character.

Pick words from the opposite page and add more of your own.

My name is...

and I am usually...

But sometimes I am...

Try this activity for all your characters. It will help you get to know them better.

Mix it up!

People with good and bad points are much more interesting than simple, one-dimensional figures. Readers will soon feel bored by a character who's always kind and gentle, but if you make her sometimes snobbish or stubborn, they'll enjoy her story much more.

Words for feelings

If you want to show your characters in depth, you'll find that overused words, like *happy* and *sad*, just aren't precise enough to express their feelings. These pages are filled with words to help you convey a range of emotions.

Instead of **happy**, try...

cheerful joyful
contented
delighted
walking on air
light-hearted
jolly ecstatic
jubilant
in good spirits

Some other words for **sad**

down in the dumps
melancholy wretched
miserable depressed
sorrowful mournful
heartbroken gloomy
grief-stricken

Alternatives for **scared**

panic-stricken
scared stiff fearful
frightened
afraid horror-struck
terrified petrified

Rather than **surprised**, use...

staggered
amazed
startled bowled over
stunned
astounded
astonished
gobsmacked

Alternatives for **angry**

enraged

furious   livid

seething

seeing red

raging   irate

fuming

Instead of **annoyed**, try...

maddened   grumpy

vexed   irritated

crotchety   peeved

exasperated   miffed

Other ways of saying **confused**

bewildered

flummoxed

flustered   dazed

perplexed

baffled   puzzled

mystified

Some other words for **worried**

on edge   nervous

tense   fretful

jittery   anxious

uneasy   agitated

Rather than **tired**, use...

shattered   sleepy

worn-out   drowsy

exhausted

weary

ready to drop   dead tired

Add some more words for feelings here.

Now go back and circle the words you like best.

Writing dialogue

Characters really come to life when they start to speak. But how do you write dialogue that's lively and realistic?

Start by listening carefully to conversations. Notice how often people leave sentences unfinished and interrupt each other.

Did you see that sign, Jake?

What sign?

unfinished sentence

It said...

Don't talk now, I'm trying to concentrate.

interruption

But Jake...

DANGER!

ZOMBIES

AHEAD

Sorry, can't talk now.

Not now, Joe. I'm busy.

But...

You can use this space to jot down snippets of conversation you've overheard.

You might hear conversations in a supermarket, on a bus or in the park.

There are some useful rules for writing speech. Follow the guidelines below to make your dialogue easy to read.

"We're in trouble now," said Jake. "How did this happen?"

Use speech marks to show when a speech begins and ends.

"Well, I..." Joe began.

Start a new line when a new person starts talking.

"You could have warned me!" snapped Jake.

Punctuation marks go inside the closing speech marks.

"Well, I did try, but..."

You don't always need to say who's talking.

"What do we do now?" asked Jake. "Tell me that!"

Don't start a new line if the same person keeps talking.

"Maybe..."

Use three dots to show a speech is unfinished.

"I really wish," said Jake, "that you could be more helpful."

Start a continued sentence like this with a lower-case letter.

"And I wish you would let me finish what I'm saying!"

Turn the page to find out more about dialogue.

Look at this conversation between
a waitress and a customer:

"Welcome to the Pizza Party House,"
said the waitress. "Can I tempt you with
one of our delectable toppings?"

"Thank you, but no," Max replied.
"I want something very plain."

"I can't believe that!" the waitress exclaimed.

"Just cheese, please," Max insisted.

"How about our tropical island option?
Five exotic fruits and three types of sausage?"

"Eurgh!" said Max. "That sounds..."

"Delicious! I know," the waitress interrupted.
"I'll be back very soon with your meal."

"Don't forget I want a VERY PLAIN PIZZA,"
Max called after her.

Plain!

You can create some
great comic effects
by showing that
people don't always
listen to each other.

44

What do you think the characters will say when the waitress brings Max's pizza? (The words on this page could help.) You could just show a dialogue between the waitress and Max, or another customer might join in.

calamity

mix-up

misunderstanding

inedible

revolting

finest ingredients

give it a try

Live dangerously!

pleasant surprise

demand to see the manager

Remember!

Keep speeches short and show the speakers interrupting each other.

Turn back to page 43 for help on showing speech.

GULP!

Putting yourself in the story

Sometimes, the main character in a story is **<u>YOU</u>**!
How would you introduce yourself to your readers?

1 Begin with first impressions.
What do people notice about you?

2 Describe your face and hair, and the clothes
you like to wear.

3 Choose some words to sum up your personality
– the good parts and the not so good!

You'll find lots of useful words on pages 32 to 39.

My self-portrait

Make a list of words like
these to get you started.

Write your description here.

spindly

curly hair

friendly

giant
sneakers

button
nose

stubborn

Let me introduce myself...

Use this space for your list.

Setting the scene

whistling wind

blazing sun

scorching sand

Use your senses!

The best way to create a convincing story setting is to draw on all your senses – sight, hearing, touch, smell, and even taste. This will help your readers imagine they're really there.

painted walls

patterned wallpaper

family photos

Try it yourself

Pretend you're an explorer in your own home. Grab a notebook and wander around, jotting down words and phrases.

thick carpet

bare boards

padded sofa

wooden chair

barking dog

blaring tv

muffled voices

burned toast

yesterday's dinner

aroma of coffee

bubbling soup

I CAN SEE...

What's close-up and what's far away?
(Describe what you see inside and outside.)

I CAN HEAR...

Are the sounds loud or quiet?

I CAN FEEL...   Are you hot or cold? What's underneath your feet?

_____

_____

_____

_____

_____

I CAN SMELL AND TASTE...   Are the smells strong or faint?

_____

_____

_____

_____

_____

_____

scudding clouds

faraway hills

birdsong

buzzing bees

droning traffic

wind in the trees

fluttering butterflies

scent of flowers

tickly grass

Lost in a dream world

Somehow, you've found yourself inside a dream world.
Can you use all your senses to describe the scene?

Maybe it's a midnight forest, a secret garden or a mysterious mansion?

_____

_____

_____

_____

_____

_____

_____

Tropical rainforest

Two explorers are lost deep inside a rainforest. Can you use strong, descriptive words to help your readers imagine the scene?

Use these pages to describe what the explorers SEE, FEEL, SMELL and TASTE.

canopy
shady
dense

lush

towering trees
tendrils
murky

Remember to describe colors and shapes.

tangled creepers
ferns
orchids
moss

Peering through the gloom, Elroy saw...

Frida struggled to breathe. The air felt...

damp
muggy
humid
steamy
sticky
scratchy
clinging
putrid
rotten
stinking

What does Frida feel against her skin, and what can she smell and taste in the air?

slimy
slippery
squelchy
boggy
undergrowth

Continued...

FOCUS on SOUND and MOVEMENT on these two pages.

dancing butterflies

hover

Concentrate first on SMALL sounds and movements.

dangle

slither

whining mosquitoes

buzz

flit

GRUNT

CHATTER

BURBLE

GURGLE

scuttle

wiggle

scurry

CROAK

Elroy stood very still, listening hard.
He noticed...

Now write about BIG movements and LOUD noises!

Frida crashed on ahead. SUDDENLY...

SHRIEK dive

swoop

SCREECH

SQUAWK

sting

bite

lurk

stalk

prowl

ROAR

spring

pounce

snap gulp

swallow

SPLASH

53

Sandy desert

You've been trudging for days through a vast, sandy desert. Use these pages to describe what you see, hear and feel.

You could write a description or make up a story.

far
horizon

stunted shrubs

endless dunes

delirious

blistering

dazzling

heat haze

What's close up and what can you see and hear in the distance?

viper

desert rat

distant howls

jackal

whistling wind

lizard

crimson glow

camel train

cloudless

nomads

What is night like in the desert?

sinking sun

brilliant stars

freezing cold

oasis

trickle

gurgle

welcoming shade

mirage

Do you reach an oasis or is it an illusion?

scorpion

scorching sand

Busy city

You're on a crowded street, hemmed in by people and traffic. Can you use all your senses to describe what's happening?

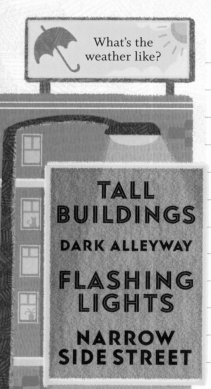

What's the weather like?

TALL BUILDINGS

DARK ALLEYWAY

FLASHING LIGHTS

NARROW SIDE STREET

What buildings can you see?

jostling

hurrying

sea of faces

exhaust fumes
engines revving

WINDOW DISPLAYS

MANNEQUINS

GIANT BILLBOARDS

PEELING POSTERS

Zoom in closer

Try zooming in on a detail of a busy scene. Maybe a lost dog goes racing through the crowds?

horns blaring

sirens wailing

What do you hear immediately? Which sounds take longer to notice?

pigeons pecking

drifts of garbage

fast food seller

Under the sea

Imagine you're a diver exploring an undersea world. What do you see?

tentacles

schools of fish

delicate seahorse

Don't forget to describe the sound of your own breathing.

darting creatures

waving seaweed

spiky coral

rotting timbers

barnacle-encrusted

drifting jellyfish

fluorescent   vivid colors

Words for stories

free fall

lost in space

shooting star

Voyage into space

Write your story
title here.

A spaceship is hurtling towards a distant planet. The crew thinks it's uninhabited, but they're in for a BIG SURPRISE...

Use the words on the next five pages to help you write about the astronauts' adventures.

QUESTIONS TO ASK YOURSELF:

- What can the crew see from their spaceship?

- How do they feel about their mission? (You could concentrate on just one or two astronauts.)

- How does the landing go?

- What are their first impressions of the planet? (Give it an interesting name.)

- What do the inhabitants look like – and how do they speak and move?

- Do the inhabitants and astronauts make friends?

- Are the astronauts happy or sad to leave?

orbit *flight path* mission

commander
many moons
comet
black hole
deep space
galaxy

shooting star
space shuttle
spacesuit
cramped
homesick
dehydrated food

weightless
zero gravity

Continued...

Do your research!

Books, movies and websites will provide lots of useful words and give you some great story ideas too.

crater

crash

soft landing

rocky

barren

canyon

extraterrestrials

aliens

insect-like

eyes on stalks

emerald green

inquisitive

glowing

You could make up words for the inhabitants to say.

BLIP BLEEP

violet sky

swirling clouds

dust storm

Continued...

vaporize

ZAP!

levitate dematerialize

laser gun

guided tour

meet the family

making friends

domed city

hitch a lift

BLAST OFF!

rocket boosters

zoom

burn up

re-entry

splash landing

quarantine

Home again

Do your characters make it safely back to Earth? Are they relieved to be home or do they dream of more space adventures?

School story

Imagine you're starting at a new school. It could be a school like yours, or it could be somewhere you've invented.

Try writing your story in the form of a diary or as a series of daily messages to a friend. Use the words on these pages to help you describe what happens each day and how life changes for you.

Write your story title here.

....

Monday: My First Day!!!

QUESTIONS TO ASK YOURSELF:

- What kind of school is it? (Give it a name.)
- What are your first impressions of your new school?
- What are the teachers like?
- Which lessons do you like best?
- Is it easy to make friends?
- Do you get into trouble?

school bus
excited
bewildered
nervous
uniform
imposing
entrance
smell of
school lunches
hallway
lockers
yelling and
shoving
whispering
giggling
loudspeaker
assembly
principal
class photo
noticeboard

Continued...

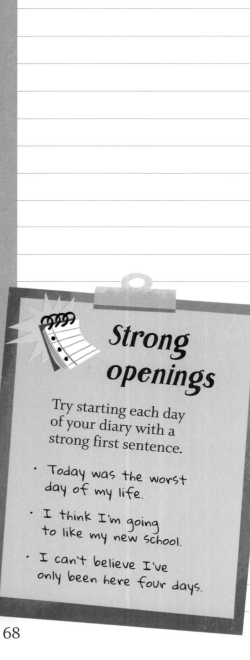

Strong openings

Try starting each day of your diary with a strong first sentence.

- Today was the worst day of my life.

- I think I'm going to like my new school.

- I can't believe I've only been here four days.

classroom
teacher's pet
class clown
saved by the bell
cafeteria
library
gym
running track
team captain
drama club

leading
role

tournament
soccer practice

Continued...

discipline
detention
schedule
prize

scholarship *exam*

straight *As*
homework
research

chemistry lab

apparatus
experiment
EXPLOSION!

Boarding school story

Your story could be set in an old-fashioned boarding school. Here are some words to get you started:

DINING HALL
DORMITORY
PREFECT
HOUSE CAPTAIN
BLAZER
MIDNIGHT FEAST
FIRE ALARM

Fantasy tale

Would you like to create a tale of mystery and magic? You'll find enticing fantasy words on the next few pages.

You can write an original story, or you could give a twist to a classic fairy tale. Imagine what would happen if Sleeping Beauty was a PRINCE and a daring princess hacked her way through the forest to rescue him!

Write your story title here.

enchanted castle

throne room

bedchamber

glass carriage

dungeon

maze

troll

fairy godmother

hobgoblin

ogre

magician

gnome

72

wicked wizard

fire-breathing
dragon

busy
elves

evil witch

Once upon a time...

Everyone knows the classic
fairy-tale opening, but why not
begin with a SURPRISE instead?

playful pixies

mysterious
forest

hollow trunk   giant toadstool

Continued...

leafy glade

deadly nightshade

impenetrable
thicket

lonely
cottage

diamond ring

jewel-encrusted
goblet

**poisoned
apple**

*flying
carpet*

broomstick

everlasting spell

potion

incantation

wand

speaking mirror

magic lamp

FEE FI
FO FUM!

cloak of
invisibility

three wishes
ancient curse
special powers
secret quest

ABRACADABRA!

HOCUS
POCUS!

Magic words will add
enchantment to your tale.

Haunted house

Can you write a story about what happens next, using vivid words to create a creepy mood?

It was almost midnight when the friends spotted the ruined house. Just the sight of it filled them with dread, but they were desperate for somewhere to spend the night…

Use this space for your story title.

....

QUESTIONS TO ASK YOURSELF:

- Who are the friends and why are they out so late? (Give them names and contrasting personalities.)

- What do they notice first about the house?

- What do they see through the windows?

- What happens when they step inside? (Remember to describe smells and sounds.)

- Do they come face to face with any ghosts?

- Are the ghosts friendly or threatening?

Building tension

Aim to build up tension in your story by starting off with some false alarms.

Ivy held her breath as the door creaked open... but it was only the wind.

eerie

crumbling

shadowy

ghoulish

flickering lights

phantom

goosebumps

spine-chilling

You will need to decide if the house is really haunted, or whether the friends are just imagining things.

Continued...

Spooky sounds

Words such as THUMP, CREAK and MURMUR sound like the noises they describe – and will make your story seem extra realistic.

CRASH

THUD

RUSTLE

CLATTER

KNOCK TINKLE

78

clank

rattle

GROAN

wail

footsteps

cobwebs

icy drafts

musty

moldy

ramshackle

Continued...

chiming clock

apparition

poltergeist

beckon

drift

glide

floating furniture

cracked mirror

trap door

grand staircase

The next morning...

Your final scene could take place the following morning, as the friends recover from their night of terror.

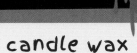

THINK ABOUT:

- What happens when morning comes?
- Does the house look different in daylight?
- Do the friends manage to find their way home?
- How does it feel to be home?

candle wax
flapping
curtains

layers of dust

Shipwrecked!

Your ship is sailing through calm seas when suddenly you notice some menacing thunderclouds. In minutes, you are being hurled across the deck. Can you survive? Or will you end up in a watery grave?

QUESTIONS:

- Why are you on a ship and where are you heading?
- What happens to the ship and are you thrown into the waves?
- Do you reach an island?
- Do you face more dangers?
- Do you make it home safely?

SHIP WORDS

cabin

captain

rigging

mast

hammock

STORM WORDS

inky sky

forked lightning

thunderclap

torrential rain

colossal waves

Continued...

shudder

lurch   splinter

treacherous currents
shark-infested waters

capsize

clinging to the wreckage

castaway
silvery sand
blue lagoon
coral reef
desert island

erupting volcano

quicksand
heatstroke
smoke signals
message in a bottle

Animal adventure

Have you ever tried writing an animal story? You could follow the adventures of a mischievous pony or describe what happens to a runaway family pet.

You will need to picture how your animal character looks and moves.

feathery

flutter

sleek

glossy

fluffy

shaggy

gnaw

nibble

graze

nuzzle

What does your animal hero see, hear, smell and feel?

Write your animal hero's name here.

.... 's story..

WHIMPER

YELP

PURR

GROWL

TWEET

Animal sounds will add drama to your story.

WHINNY

gallop
prance
canter
bolt
buck

NEIGH

bridle
saddle
stirrups

slink
sidle
crouch
cower
cringe
scamper

WOOF!

SNUFFLE

Continued...

People-watching

It's interesting to show humans through animals' eyes. Try imagining what your pet REALLY thinks of you...

dodge

chase

hurtle

freedom at last!

matted fur

bedraggled

dejected

spit

scratch

bared teeth

rolling eyes

arched back

lucky escape

race to safety

Facing danger

You could show your animal hero facing some kind of danger. But try to end your story on a happy note!

A dream come true

Use this space for your story title.

Do you have a secret dream? Maybe you'd like to sing in a band, win a competition or join a top team? You can use these pages to imagine what would happen if you achieved your goal.

lifelong
ambition
constant practice
star quality

QUESTIONS:

- What is your dream and what sparked it off?
- What did you do to help your dream come true? (Maybe you trained incredibly hard.)
- Did some people help you?
- What setbacks did you face? (Maybe you had to beat some determined rivals.)
- How did you feel when you achieved your ambition?

GOAL!

mentor
coach
warm-up
semi-finals
deciding
match
audition
contestants
rehearsal
judging panel
talent show
quaking
with nerves
quietly
confident
well
prepared

runner-up
bad loser

91

champion
first prize
winning goal
top score
podium
lap of honor
proud
tearful
congratulate
celebrate
rapturous
cheering
waves of
applause

ENCORE!

BRAVO!

HOORAY!

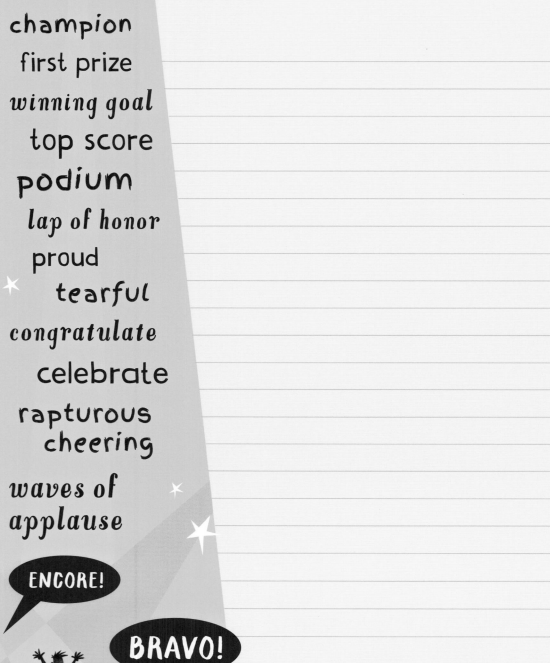

My treasure chest of words and phrases

Here are some pages for you to fill with **remarkable** words and phrases.

Add to them whenever you find a word you like and use them for **inspiration** to create **exceptional stories!**

Shiver me timbers! What spectacular words!

gleaming

glimmering

glinting

Continued...

Some word-collecting tips

- Carry a notebook to jot down words and phrases you like. Later, you can transfer them to this book.

- Copy out words and passages you've spotted in your reading.

- Try out sentences and phrases of your own.

- Make notes on how you could use the words and phrases in your stories.

You could add some sketches here too.

The more fun you have with words, the better your stories will be!

I'm just wild about words!

THE REST OF THE TEAM BEHIND THIS BOOK...

IMAGINATIVE DESIGNS by
Yasmin Faulkner, Pete Taylor and Keith Newell

PAINSTAKING PROOFREADING by
Kristie Pickersgill

EXPERT EDITING by
Felicity Brooks

American edition edited by Carrie Armstrong

At Usborne Quicklinks we have collected lots more ideas
to help you with your writing. Find out more on page 7.